ARTISTIC · CI

THE · MEDAL · IN · BRITAIN · 1880-1918

PHILIP ATTWOOD

Published for the
Trustees of the British Museum by
British Museum Press

Published by British Museum Press
a division of British Museum Publications Limited
46 Bloomsbury Street, London WC1B 3QQ

British Library Cataloguing in Publication Data
A catalogue record for this book is
available from the British Library

ISBN 0-7141-0874-X

The catalogue for this British Museum travelling exhibition
has been supported by the Henry Moore Sculpture Trust.
Additional support for the exhibition and catalogue has been
received from the UK Numismatic Trust and Glendining's

Front cover: Margherita di Prato, 1886, by Maria Zambaco (Part 2, no. 12)
Back cover: Richard Phene Spiers (reverse), 1905, by Edouard Lanteri (Part 4, no. 14)
Title page: Head of a man, by Alphonse Legros (Part 1, no. 9)
Contents page: Cambridge history prize medal, by Edward Poynter (Part 1, no. 14)

Editorial assistance: Sarah Derry, Margaret Massey
Photography: Charles Howson, Jerome Perkins, David Webb
Cover design: Ann Lumley
Exhibition design: Ann Lumley, Geoffrey Pickup, Julia Walton

Printed in Great Britain by The Bath Press, Avon

Contents

Introduction

Throughout the greater part of the nineteenth century, British medal design had been dominated by William Wyon. Engraver at the Royal Mint from 1816 and chief-engraver from 1828 until his death in 1851, he brought to the medal the grace and sureness of line that he admired in the work of the Neo-classical sculptor and illustrator John Flaxman. But the style, imitated by his son Leonard and by countless lesser figures, had by the 1880s become stale, with idealisation often translated into insipidness, and simplicity into banality. A taste for naturalistic detail, which in the 1840s and 1850s had resulted in some charming medals, perhaps best exemplified by those commissioned by the various railway companies (Wyon had himself produced a splendid medal for the Newcastle & Carlisle Railway), was also in decline. The Art-Union of London continued its series of medals celebrating the great names in the history of British art, each portraying an artist on one side and a celebrated work - a painting, sculpture or building - on the other, while the Corporation of the City of London issued medals in honour of the opening of a new bridge or the visit of a foreign monarch. But the vast majority of medals were cheap souvenir pieces issued as speculative ventures by private mints, for which technological improvements were of greater import than artistic standards. The question which began to be asked in the 1880s was how to revive an art which had degenerated into a manufacture.

Different solutions emerged. But it was Alphonse Legros who was universally recognised as the principal instigator of the late-nineteenth-century revival of the medal in Britain. Born in Dijon and trained as a painter there and in Paris, Legros, encouraged by Whistler, had come to England in 1863, in search of commissions. He had taught for a time at the National Art-Training Schools in South Kensington before securing, with the help of the painter Edward Poynter, the post of Slade Professor of Art at the University of London. This was in 1876. His first medals belong to 1881. As a painter who turned to medal-work in his mid forties, Legros' artistic career follows closely that of Antonio Pisanello, the Italian Renaissance artist credited with making the earliest medals. His medals, too, owe much to the example of Pisanello, whose work he saw displayed in the British Museum only a few hundred yards from the Slade School. Large, cast in bronze, and issued in small editions, they could not have been more different from the struck medals turned out in their thousands by the manufacturers of Birmingham and London.

The casting process, in which the medal is produced by pouring molten metal into a hollow mould made from the artist's model, had only rarely enjoyed any popularity in Britain, notably in the seventeenth century when another French man, Claude Warin, and the brothers Thomas and Abraham Simon produced a number of celebrated portrait medals. The eighteenth and nineteenth centuries had seen the total domination of the struck medal, produced by mechanical presses in the manner of coinage. Legros' cast medals were a deliberate reversion to an older tradition, and constitute a significant development in the history of the medal in Britain. By 1885 the numismatist Reginald Stuart Poole was able to write: 'In our times, thanks to the genius of Professor Legros, the cast medal has been revived ... and the artist has recovered the advantage over the mechanic which is at once his due, and which is the only guarantee of a really worthy issue of medals'.

Just as Legros' larger sculptural works, which he also began to make in the 1880s, were influenced by the example of his French contemporaries, so his medals reveal an awareness not only of the Italian Renaissance medal but also of the medallic tradition of his native land. The subject of his life-size sculpture of a seated woman in peasant costume with a child on

1. Gustave Deloye: Alphonse Legros, 1887, cast bronze, 108mm, British Museum

her lap, entitled *The sailor's wife*, was doubtless suggested by the numerous similar works by Jules Dalou, who had studied alongside Legros and Rodin in the late 1850s and, a refugee from the Paris commune, had lived and worked in London from 1871 to 1880. Similarly, Legros cannot have been unaware of the work of Pierre Jean David d'Angers, whose extensive gallery of cast medallic portraits included Victor Hugo, George Sand and Theophile Gautier. The medium remained popular in France throughout the nineteenth century, and indeed Legros himself was portrayed in this form by Gustave Deloye in 1887 (fig. 1).

Legros' desire to make a clean break with the British tradition is highlighted by his refusal to entrust their casting to an English foundry. Instead, he sent his models, both for medals and the larger sculptures, to be cast in Paris. In a letter of 30 October 1881 to his friend Rodin, announcing the imminent arrival of three of his earliest models for medals (including that of Constantine Ionides, Part 1, no. 1), the artist was at pains to point out that a smooth circumference and polished surface should be avoided: 'You will be kind enough to advise the person who does the work not to do any retouching, neither with glass-paper or anything else, nor to regularise the edges'. His antipathy to the neo-classical tradition is exemplified by his removal of the wreath which, as a traditional attribute of the poet, adorned the head of Tennyson in his pencil sketch for a medal (fig. 2). In the medal itself (Part 1, no. 2)), the wreath has gone. No accessories are allowed to distract the viewer from the penetrating and uncompromising portrait.

Other sculptors and painters, encouraged by Legros' example, began to explore the potential of the cast medal. Foremost amongst them was Edward Poynter, Legros' friend from his student days in Paris, already celebrated for his paintings recreating life in the ancient world. Poynter had worked in many media and had, in the 1870s, produced designs

2. Alphonse Legros: Alfred Tennyson, pencil, Victoria and Albert Museum

for the reverses of two official medals - the army's 'best shot' medal and the award to those who had seen action in the Second Ashanti War - but his cast medals all belong to the 1880s. Another artist who worked in many diverse media, William Blake Richmond, was also inspired to take up the cast medal, as were two painters of the St John's Wood Clique, John Evan Hodgson and William Frederick Yeames, the latter remembered principally for his painting of innocence assailed, *And when did you last see your father?*

In 1885 these artists joined with a number of other painters (including Frederic Leighton), sculptors (including Edgar Boehm and William Hamo Thornycroft), die-engravers, art historians and numismatists to found a Society of Medallists, 'for the encouragement of the art of designing and making medals'. The formation of the Society was announced in *The Times* on 23 May 1885. The deputy master of the Royal Mint, Charles Fremantle, served as the Society's president, but the driving force in its early days was one of its secretaries, the keeper of coins and medals at the British Museum, Reginald Stuart Poole, whose words in praise of Legros we have already quoted.

One of the Society's first acts was to stage a display at the International Inventions Exhibition, then being held in South Kensington. Alongside the examples of ancient and modern coinage and contemporary struck medals from Austria and Britain were cast medals by Legros, Poynter, Richmond, Hodgson, Yeames, Hamo Thornycroft, and others. Amongst Richmond's subjects were Legros and Burne-Jones, while Hodgson showed a medal of his wife with a somewhat enigmatic reverse of a cat and a fiddle. A selection of cast medals of the fifteenth, sixteenth and seventeenth centuries, borrowed from the dealers Rollin and Feuardent, identifies those medallists considered by the organisers worthy of emulation: Pisanello and Bertoldo di Giovanni in the fifteenth century, Cellini and Steven van Herwijck (then known incorrectly as Stephen of Holland) in the sixteenth century, and Dupré, Warin, Briot and Rawlins in the seventeenth.

Another case in the Society's display held a selection of cast medals produced by Legros' students at the Slade School. Legros had introduced the subject to his students the year after he had taken it up himself, and it remained on the curriculum until his resignation from the

School in 1892. The students were encouraged to visit the exhibition of Italian Renaissance medals in the King's Library at the British Museum, and a number of plaster casts made from those medals were acquired for the school. Moreover, Poole was invited to lecture to the students on the art of making medals. He offered the proceeds from these lectures as prizes for medals, and it was the results of this competition that were shown in the 1885 display.

Whereas the majority of Legros' medals are one-sided (in this he followed the contemporary French fashion) or have a reverse bearing simply a short inscription, the students were from the beginning encouraged to give their medals emblematic reverses in the manner of the Italian medallists of the Renaissance. In the competition of 1885, one of the conditions was that each medal should have 'on one side a portrait, and on the other some

3. Antonio Pisanello: Leonello d'Este (reverse), 1444, cast bronze, 101mm, British Museum

design illustrative either of the character, profession, or life of the person portrayed'. A comparison between, say, the reverse of Pisanello's medal of Leonello d'Este of 1444 (fig. 3) and the work of the Casella sisters (Part 2, nos. 4-6) shows just how closely some of the students relied on the earlier artist at the beginning of their careers.

The Society of Medallists continued to display work and offer prizes throughout the 1880s. Although some artists produced no more medals once the initial surge of activity had abated, interest in the cast medal was maintained by several of Legros' women students, and by the sculptor Edouard Lanteri who made his first medals in 1888. Lanteri had come to England from Paris, like Legros, in search of commissions. Arriving in 1872, he obtained the position of assistant to Boehm on the recommendation of Dalou, and, when Dalou returned to France, succeeded him as Master of Modelling at the South Kensington schools. Although he was later to produce models also for struck medals, he always remained hostile to the mechanical aspect of the struck medal, writing in 1904 of the 'petty effect' which, he maintained, resulted from the mechanical reduction of a model conceived in a larger proportion. His position as teacher at South Kensington (latterly the Royal College of Art) allowed him to introduce a generation of students to medal work, and made his contribution to the revival of the cast medal second only to that of Legros.

By the late 1880s the casting process was no longer restricted to personal medals. In 1890 the Royal Geographical Society took the unusual step of commissioning a cast medal for presentation to the explorer Stanley (Part 2, no. 17), and, when the Royal Astronomical Society instituted a new prize medal in 1896, it too was cast (Part 2, no. 16).

By this time, however, the struck medal also offered an alternative to the hackneyed and debased classicism of previous decades. The radical changes that befell the struck medal in the 1890s were set in motion by the celebrated and temperamental sculptor Alfred Gilbert. Working in Italy, Gilbert had, like Legros, produced his first medal, a cast medal of the painter Matthew Ridley Corbet, in 1881. In 1885 he delivered a course of lectures on the subject of casting at London's Royal School of Mines, of which the portions relating to medals were subsequently printed in the Royal Mint's *Annual Report*. But his cast medals were few and not well known, and it was instead a struck medal, commissioned from him by the Art-Union of London in 1887 (Part 3, no. 16), that most influenced younger medallists. The obverse of the medal carries one of the two medallic portraits of Victoria executed by Gilbert in the queen's jubilee year (for the other, see fig. 4); the reverse has, along with a

4. *Alfred Gilbert: Queen Victoria, 1887, struck gold, 46mm, private collection*

legend quite inappropriate for a medal celebrating the longevity of the queen's reign, an extraordinary rendition of the ship of art. The romantic imagery of this medal, its softly modelled forms and matt surfaces, all show clearly the influence of contemporary French medallists such as Jules Chaplain and Oscar Roty, and were much imitated.

Many of those sculptors who, in the 1880s and 1890s, followed Gilbert's example in their larger-scale work, and thereby participated in what came to be known as the 'New Sculpture' movement, also followed his medallic example. The partiality of the New Sculptors for modelling in wax and clay lent itself readily to the production of struck medals, for the increased sophistication of the reducing machine enabled a die to be produced from a cast of an artist's model, with only the minimum intervention on the part of a die-engraver. The Royal Mint's policy of seeking designs for both coins and medals from artists not connected with the Mint continued, undeterred by the ridicule which greeted Edgar Boehm's 1887 jubilee coinage, and in the early years of this century gave the sculptors Gilbert Bayes and William Reynolds-Stephens the opportunity to produce models for official awards (Part 4, nos. 3 and 4). The matt surface favoured by the artists of the New Sculpture, which allows the viewer better to appreciate the forms of the medal, undistracted by reflections, became standard, with the deputy master of the Royal Mint writing in 1897: 'A highly polished table is not so agreeable or artistic in finish as a dull table'. By 1912 even the Education Committee of the London County Council was convinced, and from that date its school attendance medals came in an 'artistic' matt finish.

5. Alphonse Legros: Charles Ricketts, 1897, cast bronze, 64mm, Ashmolean Museum

The French influence discernible in the works, medallic and otherwise, of the New Sculptors, many of whom had studied in Paris, is also apparent in the work of Frank Bowcher, who was especially fond of the plaquette format first used by Oscar Roty in 1880. The years following the First World War saw a reaction against the soft-edged naturalism of these sculptors' medals in favour of a more severe, clearly defined, stylised manner. This development was encouraged by Robert Johnson, deputy master of the Royal Mint from 1922, who insisted that sculptors could not meet the technical requirements for a successful medal, and devoted himself to the search for younger artists who would specialise in medallic work. His policy of excluding sculptors from official medal work led to some antagonism, and the Royal Society of Sculptors set up a committee, under the chairmanship of Gilbert Bayes, to monitor his activities.

But sculptors were, in any case, becoming increasingly uninterested in the possibilities offered by the medal. Established artists were inundated with commissions for war memorials. And for a younger generation, carving direct in stone was the preferred method, a sculptural technique that did not lend itself to medal work. Eric Gill wrote that rather than study modelling, the preferred technique of the New Sculptors, 'infinitely better would it be for me to go and apprentice myself to the most skilful and the most ordinary of monumental masons and learn to hack idiotic angels out of white marble'. In fact, Gill did on occasion involve himself in medal work (his favoured material for his models was boxwood), but in general the sculptors who came to the fore in the inter-war period, such as Epstein and Moore, restricted themselves to larger work, and medallists, such as Johnson's protegé Percy Metcalfe, rarely ventured outside coin and medal design. The close relationship between the medal and the other arts had come to an end.

The popularity of the cast medal lasted no longer than that of the sculptor's medal. In 1898 the Society of Medallists had been reformed with Legros as its president. Edward Lanteri, Charles Shannon and Legros' former students William Rothenstein and Charles Holroyd served on its committee, and amongst its members were Elinor Hallé, Feodora Gleichen, James Havard Thomas, Charles Ricketts (fig. 5) and the sculptor Alfred Drury. Poynter, Rodin and the Belgian sculptor Constantin Meunier were created honorary members. There were no representatives of the Royal Mint and no numismatists, and the cast medal was placed firmly in the context of the decorative arts. At the Society's exhibitions, items of jewellery and metalwork were shown alongside medals, statuettes and drawings, and its catalogues were produced by one of the art presses, probably the Vale Press which Ricketts and Shannon, inspired by the example of William Morris's Kelmscott Press, had set up in 1896.

The vogue for the cast medal in the late nineteenth and early twentieth centuries reflects closely the development of the Arts and Crafts movement. The Society of Medallists had been set up in the 1880s, the decade which saw the formation of Mackmurdo's Century Guild (1882), the Art Workers' Guild (1884), Ashbee's Guild of Handicraft and the Arts and Crafts Exhibition Society (both 1888). Both movements sought to counter a perceived decline in art. The charge of artistic barrenness, which Ruskin had levelled against the mass-produced goods of the nineteenth century, and which had become a central part of Arts and Crafts thinking, was applied to contemporary struck medals by Legros and his fellow medallists. Their solution, the adoption of the casting process, allowed the artist greater control of his or her work, obviating the need for an intermediary in the form of a die-engraver or for the use of machinery. It also rendered mass production impractical. Furthermore, it represented a return to the roots of the medallic tradition, to the example of the Italian medallists of the fifteenth century, a return which mirrors the advocacy by Morris and the Arts and Crafts artists of the Middle Ages as a source for inspiration.

Similarly, as the cause for the decline of the Arts and Crafts movement may be found, at least in part, in the scarcity of patrons willing to buy hand-crafted, and therefore more expensive, products, so the cast medal was unable to find patrons who would pay for this form of portrait in the age of the Kodak. Moreover, the fashion for the 'hand-made' appearance was on the wane, and institutions reverted to commissioning struck medals. The Society of Medallists, like many arts and crafts organisations, foundered in the years leading up to the First World War.

Whereas in Germany the war saw a flowering of the art of the cast medal, in Britain it contributed to its demise. In a letter to the *Manchester Guardian* the eminent archaeologist and numismatist Sir Arthur Evans noted the vibrancy of German medallic art and contrasted it sadly with the position in Britain: 'So far as I am aware ... there is no evidence of similar activity in this country beyond a solitary piece conveying the gallant assurance that Scarborough, despite the bombardment is "still undismayed"'. Evans's solution was to launch a competition for a struck medal commemorating the Battle of Jutland of 1916. Ironically, the work that was without a doubt the most original British contribution to the medallic art of the time was a cast medal, by Sydney Carline, celebrating the same event (Part 5, no. 21).

Although a few medallists such as Lady Harris and Theodore Spicer-Simson continued to make cast medals after the War, the former was forced to admit that 'the demand for this form of portraiture is, at present, very limited in England'. Only after the Second World War, with the medals of Fred Kormis, and more recently with those commissioned by the British Art Medal Society and executed by a wide range of artists, has the cast medal again enjoyed any popularity in Britain.

1 Alphonse Legros and the cast medal

It was Alphonse Legros (1837-1911), a French painter who had lived in London from 1863, who provided the initial stimulus for the radical changes that befell the medal in late Victorian Britain. Inspired by the Italian Renaissance medallists whose work was displayed in the British Museum, in 1881 he began making his own medals. Large, cast, and issued in small editions, Legros' medals could not have been more different from the struck medals being turned out in their thousands by the manufacturers of Birmingham and London.

Encouraged by Legros' example, other painters and sculptors began to explore the potential of the cast medal. In 1885 many of these artists joined together to form the Society of Medallists for 'the encouragement of the art of designing and making medals'.

1. Alphonse Legros
Constantine Ionides, 1881
Cast bronze, 91mm

Ionides, a wealthy merchant and prominent member of London's Greek community, was one of Legros' earliest and most valued patrons in Britain. The two men were introduced by Whistler on Legros' arrival in England in 1863. The following year George du Maurier wrote: 'Legros is making his fortune ... The Greeks are a providence to Jimmy [Whistler] and Legros, in buying their pictures'. Much of Ionides' large art collection, including paintings and prints by Legros, is now in the Victoria and Albert Museum. The Latin inscription on the reverse of this medal, C A IONIDES A LEGROS EX AMICITIA FACIEBAT MDCCCLXXXI (For C.A. Ionides, A. Legros made [me] out of friendship, 1881), testifies to the mutual regard of artist and patron. The artist's plaster model and two others were taken to Paris in 1881 by the sculptor Gustav Natorp, who was about to begin his training under Rodin. There the casting of the medal was executed by the founder Ferdinand Liard, and overseen by Rodin.

2. Alphonse Legros
Alfred Tennyson, 1881
Cast bronze, 121mm

In a preliminary sketch for the medal on a page taken from an Ionides company ledger (see fig. 2), a wreath adorns the head of the poet laureate, but in the medal this conventional attribute has gone. The stark realism of Legros' medals was not universally admired. Edmund Gosse, who considered that the characteristics that he admired in the New Sculpture were inappropriate for the 'curious and delicate' medium of the medal, called Legros' medals 'grotesque' and 'absolute failures'. Theodore Watts also misunderstood Legros' intentions, describing the medal as 'sadly lacking in beauty'. On the other hand, another writer praised the 'singular majesty and

1

2

breadth' of this portrait and that of Darwin (no. 3), and noted Legros' 'true perception of the character of the man presented' and his understanding of 'the peculiar capacities of the means employed'. The *Tennyson* and *Darwin* were amongst the first medals publicly exhibited by Legros in 1882 (in London's Thibaudeau gallery); three years later they were included in the Society of Medallists' exhibition. Like the majority of Legros' medals of the 1880s, both medals are one-sided.

3. Alphonse Legros
Charles Darwin, 1881
Cast bronze, 116mm

Inspired by what he regarded as the great naturalist's 'powerful and noble head', Legros sketched his portrait on an envelope at a meeting of the Royal Society. The *Magazine of Art* noted the influence of the medallists of the Italian Renaissance and reacted enthusiastically to the portrait: 'There never was such a head for a medal as Darwin's, and the artist has made the most of it'. The truthfulness of Legros' portrait can be gauged from a description of his father by Darwin's son: 'His face was ruddy, his eyes blue-grey under deep overhanging brows and bushy eyebrows. His high forehead was much wrinkled, but in other respects his face was not lined'.

4. Alphonse Legros
Thomas Carlyle, 1882
Cast bronze, 108mm

The distinguished essayist and historian was greatly admired by the artist, who had portrayed him in a number of etchings and a celebrated oil painting (now in the Scottish National Portrait Gallery) some years before the medal. However, the composition of the medallic portrait, in which Carlyle wears his characteristic broad-rimmed hat, is wholly new.

5. Alphonse Legros
John Stuart Mill, 1882
Cast bronze, 102mm

That Legros included amongst his subjects the philosopher Mill, who had died some nine years previously, suggests that he was contemplating the creation of a medallic gallery of great Victorians along the lines of the painted portraits of George Frederic Watts, an acquaintance of Legros from the 1860s. Medals of the poets Robert Browning and James Thomson, planned at about the same time, seem never to have been executed, but Gladstone and Cardinal Manning were included in the series.

3

5

6

8

6. Alphonse Legros
Maria Valvona, 1881
Cast bronze, 97mm

Besides portraits of famous contemporaries, in 1881-2 Legros also made medals of a number of artists' models, to whom he gave names redolent of the Renaissance. These exercises pay direct homage to the Italian medallists of the fifteenth century, who first devised and developed the cast medal as an art form.

7. Alphonse Legros
Antonio Escovedo, 1882
Cast bronze, 90mm

The portrait is, like no. 6, of an artist's model and the name fictitious.

8. Alphonse Legros
Gil de Mesa, c.1882
Cast bronze, 91mm

The portrait of this fictitious character has, unusually for one of Legros' medals, an eighteenth century appearance.

9. Alphonse Legros
Head of a man
Cast bronze, 78mm

The soft outlines of the portrait (see title page) suggest a later date than nos. 1-8 (cf. fig. 5, and Part 5, nos. 1-2), but that it belongs to the 1880s is proved by the inclusion of an example amongst the medals donated by the artist to the Musée du Luxembourg in Paris in 1889.

10. Edward Poynter
Una Caprese, 1882
Cast bronze, 145mm

The smooth finish of the medal, reflecting Poynter's classical genre paintings, contrasts with the more expressionist realism that Legros brought to both his pictures and his medals. In November 1881, during a stay on Capri, Poynter had made a profile chalk study of a girl called Rosina, which, when he turned to medal making in the following year, provided him with a suitable image for his first medal. Rosina was a celebrated model, who sat for many artists including John Singer Sargent. Like Legros, Poynter sent his medals to be cast in Paris.

VNA
CA
PRE
SE

10

11

11. Edward Poynter
Portrait of a woman, 1882
Cast bronze, 141mm

Poynter produced two variants of this unusual frontal portrait in his second medal. It has been suggested that the subject may be Violet Lindsay, a practising artist who also sat for Poynter. If the identification is correct, the heart-shaped pendant and clasps may allude to her marriage, which took place in 1882.

12. Edward Poynter
Lillie Langtry, 1882
Cast bronze, 141mm

In the late 1870s Poynter had executed a portrait in oils of the celebrated actress, and had also portrayed her as the mythical Greek princess Nausicaa. In the medal, Poynter's third, the dagger at her breast may be intended as a symbol of Tragedy. An example of the medal was amongst those exhibited by Poynter at the Royal Academy in 1884 and at the Society of Medallists' first exhibition the following year.

13. Edward Poynter
Sir Adolphus George Charles Liddell, 1883
Cast bronze, 130mm

Adolphus Liddell, a friend of Poynter and the subject of his fourth medal, belonged to the aesthetic circle known as 'The Souls'. Another prominent member, Alberta Victoria Paget, was portrayed in another medal of the same year.

12

14. Edward Poynter
Cambridge history prize medal, 1889
Electrotype, 114mm

The idealised profile of Clio, the muse of history, and the beaded border show the influence of ancient coinage (see contents page). This work is unique amongst Poynter's medals of the 1880s in that its main function is neither decorative nor commemorative.

15. William Yeames
Mary Helen Yeames, 1884
Cast bronze, 147x131mm

Yeames is remembered principally nowadays for his painting, *And when did you last see your father?* (Walker Art Gallery, Liverpool). This medal of his daughter was exhibited at the Society of Medallists' 1885 exhibition, and presented by the artist to the British Museum the following year. It would appear to be Yeames' only attempt at medal work.

16

17

16. William Hamo Thornycroft
Agatha Thornycroft, 1888
Cast bronze, 141mm

Thornycroft's first medals belong to 1882. In 1885 he exhibited a medal and two plaques at the Society of Medallists' exhibition. The medals of his wife Agatha and son Oliver (no. 17) were cast at James Moore's foundry in Thames Ditton, Surrey.

17. William Hamo Thornycroft
Oliver Thornycroft, 1888
Cast bronze, 135mm

The coarse texture and casting flaws of this medal of the sculptor's son and no. 16 suggest that Legros and Poynter were right to distrust the small scale casting abilities of British foundries. Subsequently, reduced versions of the medals of Oliver and the sculptor's daughter Joan were made, and mounted as a cloak buckle for his wife. The arts and crafts designer C.R. Ashbee was to put two medals of his parents to similar use in the 1890s.

18. Gustav Natorp
Phyllis
Cast bronze, 110mm

The German born Natorp was in his forties when he took up sculpture, studying first under Legros and, from 1881, under Rodin in Paris. The frontal female head of *Phyllis*, which was exhibited at the Society of Medallists' 1885 exhibition, may have been suggested by Legros' medal of a girl of 1881/2. The leafy forms of the head-dress and the name Phyllis (from the Greek for a leafy shoot) show that the image on this medal is symbolic.

18

19. Gustav Natorp
Robert Browning, 1888
Cast bronze, 118mm

This portrait of the poet Browning, who was to die in the following year, was exhibited at the Royal Academy in 1888. Browning's son was studying under Rodin at the same time as Natorp.

20. Edouard Lanteri
Julio Monticelli, 1888
Cast bronze, 92mm

Lanteri made his first medals in 1888. Monticelli was an Italian musician who visited England that year and played at the Crystal Palace. Whereas the other medals shown here were cast in sand, this medal was produced by the lost wax method of casting. The work was done by Conrad Bührer, a sculptor living in London, who, with his brother-in-law Alfred Gilbert, had conducted successful experiments in this long disused technique. This medal was exhibited at the Royal Academy in 1890 along with nos. 21-23.

21. Edouard Lanteri
Robert Glassby, 1888
Cast bronze, 98mm

This medal of the sculptor and medallist and assistant, along with Lanteri, to Edgar Boehm was sand cast by the firm of Broad and worked up by the artist.

22. Edouard Lanteri
Andreas Grass, 1888
Cast bronze, 70mm

23. Edouard Lanteri
B. Bertrand, 1889
Cast bronze, 72mm

Bertrand, who had taught fencing in London from the 1850s, did much to encourage the sport in Britain.

20

24. Edouard Lanteri

Sir Edgar Boehm, 1891
Cast bronze, 117mm

Lanteri became chief assistant to the celebrated sculptor Edgar Boehm on his arrival in England in 1872, and retained the position until Boehm's death in 1890. The portrait was modelled shortly before the artist's death, and the medal finished by the sculptor and cast by James Moore of Thames Ditton the following year. Behind Boehm's head is a sculptor's mallet and a sprig of laurel.

25. Edouard Lanteri

Adelaide Moore, 1893
Cast bronze, 136mm

This medal was also cast at James Moore's foundry in Thames Ditton, Surrey.

26. George Howard

Rhoda Ankaret Morpeth, 1895
Cast bronze, 114mm

George Howard, ninth earl of Carlisle, was a friend of the Pre-Raphaelites and a talented amateur painter, who produced a number of medals in the late 1880s and 1890s. Rhoda Ankaret L'Estrange had married Howard's son, Viscount Morpeth, in 1894.

23

24

2

2 'The Slade Girls'

Besides encouraging his contemporaries to produce cast medals, Legros also introduced his students at the Slade School of Art to the subject. The most positive response came from his female students, who met the challenges offered by this art form with enthusiasm. The quality of the students' work soon attracted attention, most notably in an article by Charlotte Weeks in the *Magazine of Art* entitled 'Women at Work: The Slade Girls'.

As the cast medal gained in popularity throughout the late 1880s and 1890s, the skill of these artists and the beauty of their medals attracted commissions from societies and other organisations. The artists combined their medallic activities with work in other media, and in the 1890s many exhibited at Arts and Crafts exhibitions.

4

1. Feodora Gleichen
Sir George Seymour, 1882
Cast bronze, 98mm

Gleichen studied at the Slade School from 1879 to 1884. Seymour was the artist's maternal grandfather. The low relief and weak lettering in this and other early medals by Legros' students reveal a somewhat tentative approach to the medium. The medals (nos. 1-3) were cast in Paris by Liard, and exhibited at London's Grosvenor Gallery in 1882.

2. Elinor Hallé
Charles Hallé, 1882
Cast bronze, 109mm

The artist, who studied at the Slade School from 1877 to 1883, was the daughter of the pianist Sir Charles Hallé, conductor and founder of the Hallé Orchestra. The winged figure of Music and the ornate organ evoke contemporary Pre-Raphaelite work.

3. C.P. Sainton
Prosper Sainton, 1882
Cast bronze, 90mm

The artist's father taught the violin at the Royal Academy of Music. Sainton is the only male artist whose work is represented in this section. Even taking into account the slight preponderance of women students, a result of the Slade's enlightened admissions policy, the high proportion of women who took up medals under the guidance of Legros is extraordinary.

4. Ella Casella
Jean Charcot, 1885
Cast bronze, 94mm

The reverse of this medal of the distinguished neurologist shows clearly the influence of the work of the Renaissance medallist Antonio Pisanello (for example, fig. 3). Portrait medals by Legros' students with emblematic reverses in the manner of Pisanello were displayed at the Society of Medallists' 1885 exhibition. They included this medal and nos. 6 and 7.

5

6

5. Ella Casella
*Henry Irving, c.*1885
Cast bronze, 87mm

In this superb portrait the great actor appears in the guise of an Italian prince. On the reverse the comic and tragic muses, Thalia and Melpomene, are placed in a rocky landscape.

6. Nelia Casella
Cardinal Manning, 1885
Cast bronze, 93mm

Nelia Casella's medal work is close stylistically to that of her sister Ella (nos. 4-5). The reverse of her medal of Cardinal Manning shows the Virgin enthroned, with Christ, St John and two angels.

7. Lilian Swainson (later Hamilton)
Cardinal Newman, 1885
Cast bronze, 72mm

Swainson studied at the Slade School from 1880 to 1886. The present example of this medal is uniface, but the version exhibited in 1885 had a cross on the reverse.

8. Maude Berry
Arthur Berry, 1886
Cast bronze, 87mm

The reverse of this medal of the artist's brother would suggest that he was a mathematician.

9. Lydia Gay
Bradley Hurt Alford, 1886
Cast bronze, 86mm

Gay studied at the Slade from 1882 to 1886. The reverse of her medal of a vicar shows Virtue vanquishing a gryphon, symbol of Vice.

10. Maria Zambaco
Head of a girl, 1885
Cast bronze, 116mm

Zambaco never registered at the Slade School, but her medallic work was directly inspired by Legros, whom she greatly admired. This, her first medal, was exhibited together with nos. 11-13 at the Royal Academy in 1887. Examples of all four were presented by the artist to the British Museum the same year. The reverse bears three anemones. In the late 1880s Zambaco was to leave London to study sculpture under Rodin in Paris.

8

9

11

11. Maria Zambaco
Marie Stillman, 1886
Cast bronze, 135mm

The artist and sitter were both nieces of Constantine Ionides (see Part 1, no. 1). Stillman was an accomplished painter. Both she and Zambaco were renowned for their beauty, and their appearance in drawings and paintings by Rossetti and Burne-Jones has tended to overshadow their own work. Zambaco is also well known for her passionate affair with Burne-Jones. The lily on the reverse of the medal is a symbol of purity.

12. Maria Zambaco
Margherita di Prato, 1886
Cast bronze, 118mm

The decorative aspect of Zambaco's work is seen to the full in this romantically-titled portrait of a woman with flowers entwined in her hair (see front cover).

13. Maria Zambaco
John Marshall, 1886
Cast bronze, 128mm

Marshall was professor of anatomy at the Royal Academy Schools and doctor to many artists, including Rossetti, and members of London's Greek Community. The reverse of the medal bears a pile of books, a quill pen and a wallet of surgical instruments, along with a Latin legend affirming that 'Nothing comes without work'.

14. Feodora Gleichen
Royal Agricultural Society Windsor exhibition medal, 1889
Electrotype, 77mm

This is an early example of a commissioned medal by Gleichen, whose work ranges from medals and small decorative objects to monumental statuary. She was to become the first woman to be elected a member of the Royal Society of British Sculptors.

11

15. Lilian Hamilton

Slade School, 1888

Cast bronze, 90mm

A winged female figure holding a wreath is accompanied by a Latin legend stating that 'Fortune helps the brave'.

16. Ella and Nelia Casella

Royal Astronomical Society Hannah Jackson-Gwilt medal, 1896

Cast bronze, 71mm

The Casella sisters collaborated on this prize medal, awarded every three to seven years, generally for outstanding observational work or for new discoveries. Urania, the muse of astronomy, appears on the reverse; the obverse bears a portrait of the astronomer Sir William Herschel.

17. Elinor Hallé

Royal Geographical Society Stanley medal, 1890

Cast bronze, 123mm

The Society presented a gold example of the medal to the explorer, and bronze examples to the officers who accompanied him. The obverse bears a portrait of Stanley. On the reverse an allegorical figure of Africa holds two vases from which pour the Congo and the Nile; in the background is Mount Ruwenzori, discovered by Stanley. The medals were cast by James Moore of Thames Ditton.

13

14

15

ROYAL·ASTRONOMICAL·SOCIETY·JACKSON-GWILT

16

CONGO
NILE
RVWENZORI
1887-1889

17

18

18. Feodora Gleichen
Princess Louise
Cast bronze, 104mm

Gleichen worked in a studio in the garden of St James's Palace, built for her father, Prince Victor of Hohenlohe-Langenburg, who was also a sculptor. The bulbous forms of the ship echo those in designs by Burne-Jones.

19. Lilian Hamilton
Rajah Jagah Jit Singh, c.1890
Electrotype, 128mm

Hamilton was one of the most prolific of Legros' former pupils. This portrait of the Rajah of Kapurthala is a rare example of an Indian subject. Some examples of the medal have an elephant bearing a howdah on the reverse.

20. Lilian Hamilton
John Dennistoun, c.1892
Cast bronze, 76mm

The reverse of this medal shows the continuing influence of Pisanello. It was exhibited at the Royal Academy in 1892.

21. Lilian Hamilton
Ian Hamilton, c.1895
Cast bronze, 86mm

The artist married the painter Vereker Hamilton in the late 1880s. The subject of this medal is their son.

22. Lilian Hamilton
Dorothy Swainson
Cast bronze, 70mm

The portrait is of a younger relative of the artist.

23. Lilian Hamilton
Fatma, c.1897
Cast bronze, 68mm

The subject of the medal is a young Bishareen Arab girl. The medal was exhibited at the Royal Academy in 1897.

RAJA·JAGAT·JIT·SINGH·SAHIB·BAHADUR·AHLUWALIA·RAJA·RAJAGAN·RAJA

19

·OPVS·L·HAMILTONIS·

20

·FATIMA·

23

24. Lilian Hamilton
Viscount Gort, 1897
Cast bronze, 112mm

Standish Prendergast, 4th Viscount Gort, was nearing eighty when the medal was made.

24

25. Lilian Hamilton
Lord Roberts, c.1897
Cast bronze, 114mm

A reduced version of this portrait of the military commander was later used as the obverse for medals of the Society of Miniature Rifle Clubs (see Part 4, no. 22).

26. Effie Stillman
Thomas F. Bayard, 1897
Cast bronze, 104mm

The artist, the daughter of Marie Stillman (see no. 11), did not study at the Slade School, but her medals clearly show the influence of Legros. In 1897 Stillman executed a three-dimensional bust of the retiring American ambassador as well as this medal, and later produced a full-size statue, which now stands opposite the Delaware Art Museum, Wilmington, USA.

27. Effie Stillman
Herbert Taylor Lewis, 1898
Cast bronze, 95mm

One of thirty-three known medals by Stillman, this portrait of a boy was amongst the medals exhibited by the artist at London's New Gallery in 1899.

27

3 The New Sculpture

The new approach to the medal instigated by Legros was paralleled in large scale sculpture by what came to be known as the New Sculpture. Both movements stemmed from a disenchantment with the smooth surfaces and idealised forms of the classical tradition, and stressed what the art critic Edmund Gosse called 'the individualities of the model', and 'the odd phenomena of surface'.

Practitioners of the New Sculpture such as Toft, Pomeroy and Onslow Ford modelled large cast medals, but it was a struck medal, Alfred Gilbert's subtly modelled celebration of Queen Victoria's Golden Jubilee (no. 16), that was the most influential of the New Sculptors' medals. Throughout the 1880s a wide range of artists - sculptors, painters and designers - produced designs for struck medals (nos. 7-15), but Gilbert's medal stands apart from the rest. Its romantic imagery, its soft forms and matt surfaces, and its integration of image and text were radical innovations and had an abiding influence on the medals of a younger generation of New Sculptors.

1. Albert Toft
Henry Irving, 1887
Cast bronze, 252mm
Toft, who had studied modelling under Lanteri at the South Kensington schools in 1881-3, was a successful portrait sculptor, who also produced decorative and architectural sculpture. His large portrait of the actor Irving is in the tradition of the monumental or architectural medallion.

2. Frederick Pomeroy
John Dando and Rose Sedding, 1891
Cast bronze, 157mm
This medal by Pomeroy, a leading figure in the New Sculpture movement, bears portraits of the Arts and Crafts architect Sedding and his wife. Sedding commissioned work from Pomeroy for his buildings, including the spectacular church of the Holy Trinity in Sloane Street, London, of 1890.

3. Edward Onslow Ford
George Charles Haité, 1891
Electrotype, 149x150mm
Ford was one of the outstanding figures of the New Sculpture. Haité was a distinguished painter, illustrator and decorative artist, who also wrote and lectured on art.

4. Edward Onslow Ford
Samuel Pepys Cockerell, 1891
Electrotype, 81mm
This is an electrotype reproduction of the portrait medal let into the plinth of Ford's bust of the painter Cockerell's daughter Frederica. The electrotype was acquired from the artist in 1894 by the collector Dr F. Parkes Weber, who presented it to the British Museum in 1906.

5. Unknown artist
Head of a man
Cast bronze, 137mm
Neither the artist nor the subject of this medal has been identified, but the subtle modelling of this sensitive portrait leaves no doubt as to the sculptor's skill.

6. Alfred Drury
Pearl Mary-Teresa Craigie, 1909
Electrotype, 112x64mm
Drury learned to model under Lanteri and Dalou, and produced symbolist sculptures as well as portrait busts and statuettes. Following the early death of the novelist Craigie in 1906, a portrait plaque to be erected in the library of London's University College was commissioned from the artist. The work illustrated here is a smaller version of that plaque.

2

7. Joseph Moore after Thomas Woolner
Lord Lawrence, 1882
Struck silver, 50mm

The sculptor Woolner, an original member of the Pre-Raphaelite Brotherhood, had made large portrait medallions since the late 1840s. In the early 1880s he also produced models for three medals. For this medal honouring the former governor-general of India, his model was reduced and the lettering and reverse added by the Birmingham firm of Joseph Moore, who also struck the medal.

8. Joseph Moore after Thomas Woolner
University College School, London, science fund research medal, 1882
Struck bronze, 64mm

Woolner's model for this prize medal is probably based on a work he exhibited at the Royal Academy thirty years earlier in 1852 entitled 'Design for a medal: Competition of the lever'. The physical exertion of the stocky figures departs from the contemporary taste for classical repose in struck medals.

9. Leonard Wyon after Sir John Tenniel
International Medical Congress, London, 1881
Struck bronze, 76mm

Tenniel's fame rested principally on his illustrations, including those for Lewis Carroll's *Alice* books. His design for the reverse of the medal of the seventh International Medical Congress, held in August 1881, shows Hippocrates protecting the people of the world from the looming figure of Death.

10. Neil Macphail after **Sir Noel Paton**
The Golden Jubilee of Queen Victoria, 1887
Struck white metal, 63mm

The reverse design by the Scottish painter Paton, celebrated for his paintings on fairy subjects, was created for a medal commemorating the twenty-first anniversary of the volunteer movement in 1881, and reused for this jubilee medal. St Michael stands over the three knights protecting 'the faith and homes' of Britain.

11. The Royal Mint after **Sir Frederic Leighton**
The Golden Jubilee of Queen Victoria, 1887
Struck silver, 77mm

The painter Leighton served on the committee of the Society of Medallists in its early days, but this, the official Jubilee medal struck by the Royal Mint, is the only medal for which he is known to have supplied a design. Several preparatory drawings for the reverse figures representing British arts and industries are known.

12. Allan Wyon after **Edward Poynter**
Department of Science and Art Sir Joseph Whitworth medal, 1883
Struck bronze, 56mm

In 1883 Poynter produced a cast medal of the mechanical engineer Sir Joseph Whitworth, which was similar in size and style to those medals exhibited here (Part 1, nos. 10-13). His prize medal, awarded annually for the scholarship endowed by Whitworth, was a reduced version of that medal, with a reverse supplied by the firm of Wyon.

13. Edgar Boehm
Sir Francis Drake memorial, Tavistock,
1883
Struck bronze, 52mm

Boehm's statue of Drake standing beside a globe was unveiled in Tavistock on 27 September 1883. The sculptor subsequently executed the model for the medal, which simply copies the larger work.

14. John Pinches after **Lewis Day**
International Fisheries Exhibition, London,
1883
Struck gold, 45mm

The designer and educationalist Lewis Day had produced a design for the reverse of a fisheries exhibition medal in 1881, but this elaborate composition symbolising fresh water and deep-sea fishing is altogether more assured.

P·M·T· ·CRAIGIE·
·JOHN OLIVER HOBBES·
1909.   A.DRVRY.

6

LET IT BE TRIED

8

PRO ARIS ET FOCIS

10

IN·COMMEMORATION

11

12

INTERNATIONAL FISHERIES EXHIBITION

14

1885 INTERNATIONAL INVENTIONS EXHIBITION

15

16

17

15. Leonard Wyon after **Lewis Day**
International Inventions Exhibition,
London, 1885
Struck silver, 45mm

This is Day's third and last medal
design (see no. 14). It was at this
exhibition, held in South Kensington
and visited by over three and a half
million people, that the Society of
Medallists held its first display.

16. Alfred Gilbert
The Golden Jubilee of Queen Victoria, 1887
Struck bronze, 63mm

Although other artists had made
contributions to the design of medals in
the 1880s, Gilbert was the first to
conceive the medal in its entirety,
modelling obverse as well as reverse
and composing both image and text.
Just as his sculptures had from the
early 1880s inspired the larger works of
the New Sculptors, so this medal,
commissioned by the Art-Union of
London, had a profound influence on
their medals.

17. George Frampton
The 500th anniversary of Winchester
College, 1893
Struck silver, 76mm

The college's founder, William of
Wykeham, is shown surrounded by
scholars, whilst on the other side the
chapel appears to float amongst the
trees. Frampton's sculptures clearly
show the influence of Gilbert, and
likewise this medal has the romantic
imagery and naturalistic detail,
integrated image and legend, and
uneven matt surface of Gilbert's earlier
medal (no. 16).

18

19

20

18. George Frampton
University College Liverpool George Holt medal, 1897
Struck bronze, 89mm

Holt, a Liverpool ship-owner and philanthropist, endowed the chair of physiology at the city's University College. The romanticised ship on the reverse of Frampton's medal is closer to Gilbert's ship of art (no. 16) than to the reality of contemporary Liverpool shipping.

19. George Frampton
City Imperial Volunteers, 1900
Struck bronze, 76mm

The medal celebrates the return of the City of London Imperial Volunteers from the Boer War. Symbolism (the figure of London, the trumpeting angels, and the sturdy oak branch) and realism (the figures of the soldiers) are combined in this medal issued by the Corporation of the City of London.

20. George Frampton
University of Glasgow David Logan medal
Struck bronze, 36mm

Frampton's concern with the decorative possibilities of lettering is apparent in his medals as in his larger plaques, and mirror contemporary developments in book design. The naturalism of the flora and fauna on this small medal is charming.

21. George Frampton
The Coronation of Edward VII and Queen Alexandra, 1902
Struck bronze, 52mm

The symmetrical arrangement of the trees is a device also used by Frampton on his portrait plaques.

22. William Goscombe John
Llywelyn ap Grufydd
Struck bronze, 76mm

The sculptor Goscombe John left his native city Cardiff for London, but always maintained his Welsh connections. Llywelyn, the last prince of an independent Wales, appears on one side of the medal, whilst on the other is a nightingale in a rowan tree and distant view of Snowdon.

22

23

24

23. William Goscombe John
National Eisteddfod Association, 1898
Struck bronze, 76mm; 41mm

On this medal, issued in two sizes, the sixth-century Welsh band is seen walking through an ancient landscape complete with cromlech; on the other side is the Welsh dragon.

24. William Goscombe John
University College of South Wales Alfred William Hughes medal, 1902
Struck bronze, 57mm

The medal served as an anatomy prize.

25. William Goscombe John
Thomas Edward Ellis, 1909
Struck bronze, 62mm

Ellis was a leading member of the Welsh Language Society and Liberal member of Parliament for Merionethshire from 1886 until his death in 1899.

26. William Goscombe John
Investiture of the Prince of Wales, 1911
Struck gold, silver, 34mm

Caernarvon castle, scene of the investiture, is shown on the reverse. Goscombe John also designed the investiture regalia, including the chaplet worn by the prince on the medal (now in the National Museum of Wales).

27. William Goscombe John
Cardiff School of Art Goscombe John prize medal, 1918
Struck silver, 38mm

The prize, instituted by the artist himself, was awarded for proficiency in modelling.

28. Bertram Mackennal
Olympic Games commemorative medal, 1908
Struck silver, bronze, 50mm

The Australian sculptor Mackennal studied in Melbourne, Paris and London, and settled in Britain in 1894. His official Olympic commemorative medal has a victorious Greek athlete on one side and a figure of Fame on the other.

29. Bertram Mackennal
Olympic Games prize medal, 1908
Struck bronze, 33mm

Mackennal's Olympic prize medal has an athlete being crowned with a laurel wreath on one side, and, on the other, St George, patron saint of England, host of the 1908 games.

30. Albert Toft
The Coronation of Edward VII and Queen Alexandra, 1902
Struck bronze, 35mm

The sculptures of Toft show the influence of his teacher, Lanteri, and of Gilbert. The dramatic lines of the medal and the figures of the two angels derive from Gilbert.

31. Alfred Drury
First World War memorial medal, c.1918
Struck silvered bronze, 80mm

29

30

31

4 Struck medals in the twentieth century

In the early years of the twentieth century the British medal was subject to a new wave of Continental influences. Frank Bowcher worked for six years under one of the New Sculptors, Edward Onslow Ford, but his medals are informed by the gentle lyricism of contemporary French medallic work, whilst Emil Fuchs, a Viennese sculptor who lived in London for about ten years from 1897, imbued his medals with a tender sentimentality.

More robust is the work of Legros' former students, such as Gleichen and Hamilton, and that of the younger New Sculptors, in particular C.J. Allen (Hamo Thornycroft's former assistant) and Gilbert Bayes. Herbert MacNair's extraordinary design for the reverse of the Kingsley medal (no. 25) is one of two medal designs by that artist (who was married to the sister of Charles Rennie Mackintosh's wife) and reveals his close association with the Glasgow School.

The naturalism of these sculptors' medals was displaced in the years following the First World War by the more stylised products of a generation of younger artists specialising particularly in medallic work.

2

3

4

5

1. George William de Saulles after **Thomas Brock** and William Wyon
The Diamond Jubilee of Queen Victoria, 1897
Struck silver, 55mm
   De Saulles worked as engraver at the Royal Mint from 1892 until his early death in 1903. He based his design for this official medal on William Wyon's portrait of Victoria for the coinage of 1839 (in use until 1887) and Brock's head of 1893.

2. Frank Bowcher
Music, c.1885
Cast bronze, 133mm
   Although Bowcher's fame rests on his struck medals, he also produced a number of cast pieces, such as this charming medal of Music, which was cast in Paris.

3. Frank Bowcher
Antonio Redaelli, 1890
Cast bronze, 64mm

4. Frank Bowcher
Cope and Nicol School of Painting, London
Struck silver, 57mm

5. Frank Bowcher
The Artist's wife, 1895
Electrotype, 57mm

6

7

8

9

6. Frank Bowcher
Dr F. Parkes Weber, 1899
Cast bronze, electrotype, 198x136mm; 68x47mm

Parkes Weber donated his large collection of coins and medals to the British Museum. The smaller version of this cast plaquette serves as a Royal Numismatic Society prize medal.

7. Frank Bowcher
Thomas Henry Huxley, c.1898
Struck silver, 62mm

On the reverse of this medal of the distinguished scientist a figure places a wreath on the altar of scientific knowledge. In the background is the Royal College of Science.

8. Frank Bowcher
Franco-British Exhibition, London, 1908
Struck silver, 50mm

9. Frank Bowcher
Cambridge Biblical Society, 1911
Struck bronze, 75mm

The image is borrowed from the reverse of Pisanello's medal of the humanist Pier Candido Decembrio of 1447/8. The legend translates as 'He has directed my steps'.

10. Emil Fuchs
Lord Beresford, 1899
Struck silver, 32mm

Beresford had served in the navy since boyhood. The reverse of the medal alludes to his travels: in 1899 he returned from a mission to China, and the following January was sent to the Mediterranean as second-in-command of the fleet.

11. Emil Fuchs
Queen Victoria, 1900
Struck silver, 27mm

During his years in England, Fuchs' softly-modelled naturalistic style attracted aristrocratic patrons. The queen commissioned two medals to commemorate the entry of her reign into the twentieth century. This version was intended to be presented to members of the royal family.

10

11

12

13

15

19

18

12. Emil Fuchs
Princess of Pity, 1900
Struck silver, 70x70mm

Fuchs' style suited the taste of Princess Alexandra, who specifically requested that the background to the reverse (see illustration above) should be 'soft and delicate'. The title was suggested by a lady-in-waiting.

13. Emil Fuchs
South African campaign, 1900
Struck silver, 69mm

An angel descends to carry away the body of a soldier killed in the Boer War, whilst behind a battle continues. The medal was admired by the future Edward VII, who sent an example to his sister Victoria, Empress of Germany.

14. Edouard Lanteri
Richard Phene Spiers, 1905
Struck bronze, 78x58mm

The obverse bears a portrait of this architect, who was master of the Royal Academy School of Architecture from 1870 until 1906. On the reverse is a distant view of the Athenian acropolis (see back cover).

15. Allan Gairdner Wyon
Calcutta School of Tropical Medicine Minto medal, 1914
Struck silver, 70x47mm

This prize medal takes its name from the Earl of Minto, viceroy of India from 1905 to 1910. The sculptor and medallist Wyon had worked as Hamo Thornycroft's studio assistant.

16. Joseph Fray
The Coronation of George V and Queen Mary, 1911
Silvered bronze, 72mm

Fray was a Birmingham jeweller and medallist.

17. The Bromsgrove Guild
Lincoln Art and Industrial Exhibition, 1909
Struck silver, cast bronze, 50mm

This arts and crafts organisation, based in Bromsgrove, Worcestershire, expanded into medal-work in 1909.

18. The Bromsgrove Guild
Joan of Arc, 1909
Struck bronze, 51x33mm

The medal is one of two produced by the Guild to commemorate the beatification of Joan. The saint is shown riding into Rheims, carrying a banner decorated with fleurs de lis and on which there is an apparition of the Virgin and Child. The Guild also issued a statuette of Joan.

19. The Bromsgrove Guild
The Centenary of William Crawford and Sons, 1913
Struck bronze, 70x52mm

Crawford and Sons were manufacturers of biscuits.

20. Sir Hubert Herkomer
The Royal Automobile & Associated Clubs, 1908
Struck bronze, 77mm

This is the only medal by this eminent portrait painter, who also produced wood-engravings and lithographs as well as enamel-work and designs for metal-work. He was also an enthusiastic motorist, and in 1905 had designed a silver trophy, *The Spirit of the Motorcar*, for the Munich trials.

21. Feodora Gleichen
St Thomas's Hospital Florence Nightingale medal, 1914
Struck bronze, 45mm

This prize medal, by a former student of Legros, bears a portrait of the celebrated reformer of hospital nursing.

22. Lilian Hamilton
Society of Miniature Rifle Clubs medal, 1900
Struck bronze, 30mm

The portrait on this prize medal is a reduced version of an earlier cast medal (Part 2, no. 25).

23. James Havard Thomas
University College London Rosa Morison medal, 1900
Struck bronze, 48mm

Thomas had studied sculpture in London and Paris. Morison was superintendent of the women students at University College.

24. James Havard Thomas
P. H. Emerson, 1907
Struck silver, 45mm

20

22

21

23

25

26

25. Charles John Allen and **Herbert MacNair**

Liverpool School of Tropical Medicine Mary Kingsley medal, 1903
Struck silvered bronze, 96x57mm

The reverse of this magnificent prize medal by the Scottish artist MacNair is a fine example of Glasgow School *art nouveau*. The traveller and writer Mary Kingsley had died of typhoid fever in 1900, whilst serving as a camp nurse in the Boer War.

26. Charles John Allen

The 700th anniversary of Liverpool, 1907
Struck silvered bronze, 63mm

Allen had received tuition from several of the New Sculptors, and from 1890 to 1894 acted as assistant to Hamo Thornycroft. The Liverpool medal was issued in three sizes.

27. Cecil Thomas

The Oxford millenary, 1912
Struck silver, 50mm

The medallist and gem-engraver Thomas had studied at London's Central School of Arts and Crafts. The towers and spires of Oxford are seen enclosed in the old city walls.

28. Thomas Brock

Royal Academy gold prize medal, 1910
Cast bronze, 187mm

The artist's plaster model, from which this bronze was cast, was subsequently reduced mechanically. From the resulting dies, the medals were struck. Brock has composed three figures representing the arts of painting, sculpture and architecture into a balanced design.

29. Kathleen Scott

Royal Geographical Society Peary medal, 1910
Struck bronze, 69mm

The artist was a sculptor and wife of the Antarctic explorer Robert Falcon Scott. The eagle and globe on the reverse of her medal of Peary symbolise the American's nationality and explorations respectively. A gold example was presented by the Society to the explorer in May 1910.

27

30

31

30. Gilbert Bayes
Royal Geographical Society Scott medal, 1904
Struck bronze, 69mm

Whereas in 1890 the Society had commissioned a cast medal (Part 2, no. 17), by the early 1900s it had reverted to struck issues. Bayes, whose sculptures show the influence of Gilbert and Frampton, produced a model, which was subsequently reduced by Allan Wyon. Wyon also worked on the dies, to make the definition crisper (cf. the more indistinct forms and uneven lettering of no. 31).

31. Gilbert Bayes
Royal Geographical Society Shackleton medal, 1909
Struck bronze, 69mm

In the reverse of his second medal for the Society, Bayes creates a vivid impression of the vastness of the polar region. The medal was reduced and struck by the firm of Pinches.

32. Gilbert Bayes
*Rubber Growers' Association, c.*1910
Struck bronze, 52mm

33. Gilbert Bayes
Country Life *marksmanship medal, c.*1913
Cast bronze, 38mm

This is a prize for the annual rifle competition for schools, set up by *Country Life* magazine in 1912. Bayes's handling of the planes shows his mastery of relief, even on this small scale.

34. William Reynolds-Stephens
Edward VII miners' medal (reverse), 1907
Struck silver, 33mm

The medal was instituted in 1907 to reward arts of gallantry in mines and quarries. For the reverse, Reynolds-Stephens, a prominent New Sculptor, produced a realistic design of the rescue of a miner.

35. Kathleen Scott
Edward extension medal (reverse), 1910
Struck silver, 33mm

The scope of no. 34 was extended in 1910 to include industry generally. Again, the reverse portrays an industrial accident.

32

36. Gilbert Bayes
The King's police medal (reverse), 1910
Struck silver, 36mm

For this medal, to be awarded for acts of courage by members of the police and fire brigades in Britain and the empire, the artist produced an allegorical design symbolising (with its town walls and night-watchman's lantern) civil protection.

37. Ernest Gillick
Inner Temple First World War memorial medal, 1918
Struck bronze, 51mm

Gillick was a sculptor and arts and crafts designer who also designed a number of medals.

38. Charles Leighfield Doman
First World War memorial medal, 1918
Struck silver, 76mm

Doman was a sculptor who specialised in decorative and architectural work.

33

34

35

36

38

5 Cast medals in the twentieth century

The last few years of the nineteenth century saw a resurgence of activity on the part of the Society of Medallists. Legros was now its president, and younger artists such as Charles Shannon, Charles Ricketts (see fig. 5) and Legros' former student, William Rothenstein, were actively involved, along with Hamilton, Gleichen, Hallé and other women medallists.

The art of the cast medal was kept alive in the early years of this century by these artists and medallists such as Theodore Spicer-Simson and Sydney Carline. But commissions became scarcer as the popularity of the medium waned. By the outbreak of the First World War, Legros was dead and the Society of Medallists had, like many Arts and Crafts organisations, ceased to exist. Two remarkable features, though, marked these later years: the increasingly abstract forms of Carline's medals, and the production of Carter Preston's First World War plaque in numbers unprecedented for a cast medal.

2

3

1. Alphonse Legros
Self-portrait, 1907
Cast bronze, 239x166mm

At the revival of the Society of Medallists in 1898, Legros was hailed as 'not only president, but the father and master of the rest'. This self-portrait nine years later shows the artist at the age of seventy.

2. Alphonse Legros
The Duke of Devonshire, 1898
Cast bronze, 149mm

This portrait of the prominent Liberal politician Spencer Compton Cavendish, 8th Duke of Devonshire, is one of several medals by Legros made in the late 1890s and shown at an exhibition held by the Society of Medallists in London's Dutch Gallery in 1898. The knotted serpent forms part of the Cavendish crest.

3. William Rothenstein
Auguste Rodin, 1897
Cast bronze, 137mm

In the late 1880s Rothenstein studied under Legros at the Slade School, and had then spent five years in Paris, where he met Rodin. Subsequently, he did much to publicise the work of Rodin in England. The medal portrait is based on a lithograph of 1897 subsequently published by Rothenstein as part of his *French Set*. The artist was a committee member of the revived Society of Medallists, and exhibited this medal, along with another of Paul Verlaine and drawings of both men, at the Society's 1898 exhibition.

4. Lilian Hamilton
Dorothea Beale, 1904
Cast bronze, 128x108mm

A reduced version of this portrait of the principal of Cheltenham Ladies' College was used as the obverse of a struck medal commemorating the college's fiftieth anniversary.

5. Lilian Hamilton
Jean Hamilton, 1904
Cast bronze, 110mm

Of Legros' former students, Hamilton remained most faithful to the medal, producing medallic portraits, including members of her family, into the 1920s.

6. Feodora Gleichen
Prince Louis of Battenberg, 1914
Cast bronze, 98mm

In the 1900s Gleichen concentrated increasingly on larger work, whilst other former 'Slade girls' turned to other areas of the arts and crafts, such as enamels, wax-carving and decorative plaster-work. This medal celebrates the prince's sixtieth birthday.

7. Grace Mason
Rita Roberts, 1910
Cast bronze, 247x210mm

The artist had studied at the Slade School in the late 1890s after the departure of Legros. Frampton continued to teach sculpture and modelling until 1899. The work produced under him was very different from that of Legros' students of the 1880s.

8. Ethel Bower (later Lady Harris)
Sir William Crookes, 1906
Cast bronze, 94mm

Bower studied at the South Kensington schools for six years, and in later years recalled Lanteri with gratitude as 'a master of technique and a most admirable teacher'. She portrayed him in a medal of about 1905, an example of which is now in the Musée d'Orsay, Paris. Crookes was a distinguished scientist, who worked in chemistry and physics.

4

10

11

9. Charles John Allen
University College Liverpool Hemans medal, 1900
Cast bronze, 121mm

The medal, to be awarded for a lyrical poem, was named after the early nineteenth-century poet Felicia Hemans, generally remembered nowadays only for *Casabianca* ('The boy stood on the burning deck ...'). The portrait is taken from a bust of about 1829 by Angus Fletcher (National Portrait Gallery), although the dramatic arrangement of the cloak is Allen's own. The influence of Lanteri is apparent. The reverse shows a winged figure crowning Poetry.

10. Cecil Browne
Murray Marks, 1913
Cast bronze, 87mm

Marks was an art dealer who in the 1860s and 1870s had supplied, amongst others, Whistler and Rossetti with blue and white Chinese porcelain. This medal, commissioned by friends of Marks, was one of three exhibited by the sculptor and medallist Browne at the Paris salon in 1914.

11. Harold Stabler
Sow, 1911
Cast bronze, 90mm

Stabler was principally a metal-worker, who had taught at Keswick School of Industrial Art and Liverpool University Art School, before moving to London in 1902. From 1907 he was head of the art school of the Sir John Cass Institute. He also worked in wood, stone and ceramic, and made a number of cast and struck medals.

12. Theodore Spicer-Simson
George Frederic Watts, 1904
Cast bronze, 83mm

Spicer-Simson studied at the Ecole des Beaux-Arts in Paris in the early 1890s and began exhibiting large scale sculptures, principally portrait busts, in 1896. His first medals date to 1903. Some are struck, but the artist remained throughout his life an ardent opponent of the reducing machine, and the overwhelming majority of his medals are cast. This example is of the celebrated painter Watts, who was to die aged ninety in 1905.

12

14

16

17

13. Theodore Spicer-Simson
Max Rosenheim, 1910
Cast bronze, 123mm

Rosenheim was a collector of and authority on medals.

14. Theodore Spicer-Simson
Hilda Schmidt, 1913
Cast bronze, 81mm

The vigour of Spicer-Simson's Watts medal (no. 12) is combined here with a delicacy of execution often found in the artist's medals, derived from his early years in France. Spicer-Simson continued to make portrait medals until 1950, latterly in his adopted home of America.

15. Sydney March
Sir George Livesey, 1908
Electrotype, 185mm

The medal was made at the time of Livesey's death. Engineer and philanthropist, Livesey was a proponent of profit-sharing and labour co-partnership.

16. Percival Hedley
Lily Elsie, 1907
Electrotype, 90x110mm

Hedley studied sculpture in Vienna in the 1880s. In the 1900s he spent some years in England. His plaquettes and medals include portraits of many theatrical subjects, such as Lily Elsie whose appearance in the title role of the British première of *The Merry Widow* in 1907 caused something of a sensation.

17. Cecil Thomas
Surrey Rose Club, 1909
Electrotype, 85x75mm

An example of the romanticism, informed by continental *art nouveau*, of Thomas's early work.

18. Cecil Thomas
Percy, 1909
Cast bronzed lead, 86mm

19. Sydney Carline
Harold Viscount Dillon, 1913
Cast bronze, 78mm

Carline studied at the Slade School in the 1900s. Dillon was an antiquary and, from 1892 until 1913, first curator of the armouries of the Tower of London.

19

20

21

20. Sydney Carline
Alexander Richard Rolleston Woods, 1914
Electrotype, 93mm

The influence of Pisanello is combined here with the simplified planes and decorative forms of contemporary sculpture. The reverse legend translates as: 'I scorn to change or to fear'.

21. Sydney Carline
Battle of Jutland, 1917
Electrotype, 83mm

The reverse composition, formed almost entirely from sea and smoke, is virtually abstract and something quite new in the art of the medal.

22. Edmund Dulac
Nach Hause (Going home), 1918
Cast bronze, 107mm

This medal by Dulac, best known for his book illustrations, parodies a German medal of 1914, which carried the legend 'Nach Paris'. Dulac shows the horse and rider defeated and reduced to skeletons.

23. Edward Carter Preston
First World War memorial plaque, 1918
Cast bronze, 121mm

The medal was presented to the next of kin of those who had died in the war. It has been estimated that over one million were produced, each bearing the name of the person commemorated. Carter Preston was one of a new generation of artists taken up by the Royal Mint for medallic work in the 1920s.

23

British Museum Registration Numbers

One
1. 1984-5-40-1
2. 1882-4-3-4. Presented by the artist
3. 1882-4-3-2. Presented by the artist
4. 1882-4-3-1. Presented by the artist
5. 1882-4-3-3. Presented by the artist
6. 1882-4-3-6. Presented by the artist
7. 1882-10-6-2. Presented by the artist
8. 1984-5-40-6
9. 1984-5-40-4
10. 1884-12-1-4. Presented by the artist
11. 1919-12-2-4. Presented by the executors of the artist
12. 1884-12-1-2. Presented by the artist
13. 1919-12-2-1. Presented by the executors of the artist
14. 1919-12-2-5. Presented by the executors of the artist. 1966-4-3-277. Presented by Mr W.E. Watts
15. 1886-5-11-1. Presented by the artist
16. 1906-11-3-4777. Presented by Dr F. Parkes Weber
17. 1978-7-7-1
18. M 0629
19. 1985-9-2-1
20. 1906-11-3-1602. Presented by Dr F. Parkes Weber
21. 1906-11-3-549. Presented by Dr F. Parkes Weber
22. 1977-6-15-29. Presented amonymously
23. 1977-6-15-28. Presented anonymously
24. 1906-11-3-4763. Presented by Dr F. Parkes Weber
25. 1979-10-13-2
26. 1979-12-1-1

Two
1. 1906-11-3-545. Presented by Dr F. Parkes Weber
2. 1906-11-3-546. Presented by Dr F. Parkes Weber
3. 1906-11-3-547. Presented by Dr F. Parkes Weber
4. 1887-5-3-1
5. M 6601
6. 1887-5-3-2
7. 1924-4-18-4. Presented by the artist
8. M 6599
9. M 6597
10. 1887-2-9-1. Presented by the artist
11. 1887-12-7-1. Presented by the artist
12. 1887-2-9-2. Presented by the artist
13. 1887-12-7-2. Presented by the artist
14. 1906-11-3-552. Presented by Dr F. Parkes Weber
15. 1984-6-27-20
16. 1988-7-16-2
17. 1890-12-4-1. Presented by the Royal Geographical Society. M 8761
18. 1920-2-25-1
19. 1981-9-16-4
20. 1979-9-6-1
21. 1924-4-18-6. Presented by the artist
22. 1924-4-18-5. Presented by the artist
23. 1924-4-18-7. Presented by the artist
24. 1980-5-6-4
25. 1924-4-18-3. Presented by the artist
26. 1979-10-13-3
27. 1985-8-6-1

Three
1. 1981-7-26-1
2. 1979-10-13-1
3. 1981-7-25-1
4. 1906-11-3-554. Presented by Dr F. Parkes Weber
5. 1984-6-25-1
6. 1987-7-17-7
7. 1896-2-1-1. Presented by Mrs A.L. Johnstone
8. 1882-4-6-1. Presented by Mr T. Orme
9. 1882-2-4-2. Presented by the Executive Committee of the International Medical Congress
10. 1906-11-3-622. Presented by Dr F. Parkes Weber
11. 1901-1-2-14. Presented by the Royal Mint
12. 1906-11-3-615. Presented by Dr F. Parkes Weber
13. 1887-10-9-1. Presented by the Revd E. Spencer
14. 1945-9-1-141. Presented by Mr C.A. Fremantle
15. 1906-11-3-621. Presented by Dr F. Parkes Weber
16. 1906-11-3-553. Presented by Dr F. Parkes Weber
17. 1934-3-3-10. Presented by Mr H.H. Gordon Clark. 1949-1-6-1. Presented by Mrs C. Dodgson
18. 1966-4-3-659. Presented by Mr W.E. Watts
19. 1901-10-12-1. Presented by the Corporation of the City of London
20. 1966-4-3-35. 1983-6-8-1. Presented by Mr W.E. Watts
21. 1979-5-17-72. Presented by Prof. and Mrs J. Hull Grundy. 1922-4-7-345. Presented by Mr L.A. Lawrence
22. 1982-3-4-4
23. 1983-6-8-2. 1983-6-8-3
24. 1943-4-2-2. Presented by Mr A.W. Hare
25. 1980-2-11-1
26. 1912-9-3-27. Presented by the Royal Mint 1919-5-5-1. Presented by HM Queen Mary
27. 1982-3-7-14
28. 1908-9-3-1. Presented by the Council of the British Olympic Association
29. 1908-9-3-5/6. Presented by the Council of the British Olympic Association
30. 1980-5-6-1
31. 1988-12-5-1

Four
1. 1987-6-49-20. Presented by the National Art Collections Fund. 1901-1-2-18. Presented by the Royal Mint
2. M 6979
3. 1906-11-3-1617. Presented by Dr F. Parkes Weber
4. 1894-8-3-1. Presented by the artist
5. 1906-11-3-651. Presented by Dr F. Parkes Weber
6. 1954-2-2-1. Presented by Dr F. Parkes Weber T. 324
7. 1898-10-9-1. Presented by the Huxley Memorial Committee
8. 1978-7-12-5. Presented by Prof. and Mrs J. Hull Grundy. 1954-10-4-4. Presented by Mr J.H. Watts
9. 1911-8-8-1. Presented by the artist
10. 1987-11-50-1
11. 1982-1-11-4. Presented by HRH the Duke of Gloucester
12. 1981-11-3-1
13. 1900-10-6-1. Presented by Mr H.A. Grueber M 8784
14. 1905-11-13-1. Presented by the Phene Spiers Testimonial Committee
15. 1985-5-3-1
16. 1982-7-7-3
17. 1917-2-3-1. Presented by the Bromsgrove Guild 1973-10-14-8. Presented by Mr J.M. Magee
18. 1917-2-3-2. Presented by the Bromsgrove Guild
19. 1917-2-3-3. Presented by the Bromsgrove Guild
20. 1983-6-8-4
21. 1917-3-4-1. Presented by Mr W. Minet
22. 1984-6-27-3. 1981-8-12-1. Presented by Mr E.F. Tuffrey
23. 1916-1-4-1. Presented by the artist
24. 1908-11-12-1. Presented by Mr P.H. Emerson
25. 1988-7-19-1
26. 1908-1-1-1. Presented by the Liverpool Foundation Committee
27. 1939-3-3-1. Presented by Mr F.F. Madan
28. 1987-7-17-5
29. 1910-5-5-1. Presented by the Royal Geographical Society
30. 1905-2-9-1. Presented by the Royal Geographical Society
31. 1909-10-1-1. Presented by the Royal Geographical Society
32. 1983-6-8-6
33. 1987-1-1-1. Presented by Mr C. Eimer
34. 1908-2-10-45. Presented by the Royal Mint
35. 1911-3-12-42. Presented by the Royal Mint
36. 1911-3-12-34. Presented by the Royal Mint
37. 1978-7-12-23. Presented by Prof. and Mrs J. Hull Grundy
38. 1978-7-12-62. Presented by Prof. and Mrs J. Hull Grundy

Five
1. 1984-5-44-4
2. 1984-5-40-3a; b
3. 1985-5-23-1
4. 1924-4-18-10. Presented by the artist
5. 1924-4-18-2. Presented by the artist
6. 1981-8-11-1
7. 1982-7-30-1
8. 1921-2-7-2. Presented by the artist
9. 1987-7-17-6
10. 1966-4-3-818. Presented by Mr W.E. Watts 1912-12-20-1. Presented by Mr M. Marks
11. 1912-12-8-1. Presented by the artist
12. 1917-2-8-1. Presented by Mr G.F. Hill
13. M 8752
14. 1934-1-5-9. Presented by the artist
15. 1980-9-20-2
16. 1983-12-13-3
17. 1978-12-20-43. Presented by Mr A. Thomas
18. 1978-12-20-36. Presented by Mr A. Thomas
19. 1913-12-1-1. Presented by the Trustees of the National Portrait Gallery
20. 1979-12-27-5
21. 1979-12-27-2
22. 1919-11-3-1. Presented by the artist
23. 1980-6-1-1. Presented by Mrs I. Gray

Index

The names of medallists whose work is included in the exhibition are given in bold.